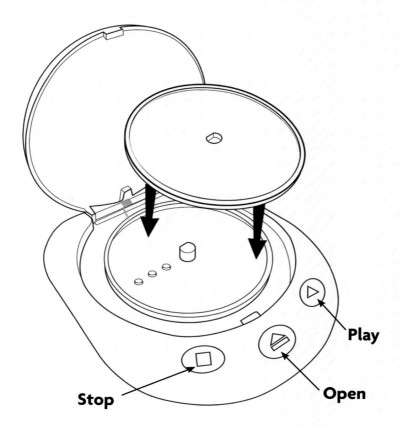

Play

Stop

Open

How to Use the Music Player

**Use your music discs to create the perfect
atmosphere for the stories as you read.**

- Each disc has a picture of a character on it. Find the disc that matches the story you are reading.

- Open the music player by pressing the middle button ⏏. Insert the disc and close the lid. When you are ready to play a tune as indicated in the story, press the button on the right ▷. To play the next tune, press the right-hand button again ▷. To stop the music at any time during play, press the left-hand button ☐.

- When the player is stopped in the middle of a tune, it will then resume that tune when the play button is pressed again.

- After a period of non-use, the player will shut off. When the play button is pressed again, the player will go back to the first tune on the disc.

Disney
Sofia the First

Royal Prep
Talent Show

written by Elizabeth Bennett

Reader's
Digest
Children's Books®

New York, New York • Montréal, Québec • Bath, United Kingdom

My name is Sofia and I'm a princess.
I go to school at the Royal Prep Academy
with all the other princes and princesses.

SONG
1

The fairies have a special announcement.
We're going to have a talent show for all
of our parents.

Everyone's excited about
the show—except for me. . . .

James decides to recite a poem.
Jun is going to play the cello.

Clio will bake her famous cupcakes.

Kamol and Amber will do a dance.

SONG
2

But what will I do? I don't have a special talent.
"Just think about what you love to do," says
my mom. "If you do what you love, your
talent will shine through."

I think about it for a while. I do love animals.
And they love me. Maybe that's my talent.

I know. Pearl the unicorn is visiting
the castle. I can teach her a trick for the
talent show. This is going to be fun!

I want to teach Pearl to dance, but it's not as easy as I thought! Pearl just wants to play. When I try to teach her the dance steps, she climbs on top of the piano!

SONG 4

Then I remember my magic amulet. It helps me talk to animals.

"What's wrong?" Pearl asks me. I tell her
about the talent show.

"Will you help me?" I ask her.

"Of course I will help!" she says.

Pearl and I work together all day
and soon I know that we're ready.

On the day of the talent show, Pearl and I go onto the stage. The music plays and we dance. Everyone cheers!

Talent shows are fun when you do what you love!

BATTERY INFORMATION

To remove or insert replaceable batteries, remove safety screw from battery compartment door. Lift and remove door. Take out and safely dispose of old batteries. Follow polarity diagram inside compartment to insert two new batteries of any of the following types: AA or LR6 or equivalent. Alkaline batteries are recommended. Put battery compartment door back and secure safety screw. Do not use excess force or an improper type or size screwdriver.

CAUTION

To ensure proper safety and operation, battery replacement must always be done by an adult. Never let a child use this product unless battery door is secure. Keep batteries away from small children and immediately dispose of any used batteries safely.

GENERAL SAFETY AND CARE

- Rechargeable batteries are not to be used in this product.
- Non-rechargeable batteries are not to be recharged.
- Different types of batteries or new and used batteries are not to be mixed.
- Batteries are to be inserted with the correct polarity.
- Exhausted batteries are to be removed from the toy.
- The supply terminals are not to be short-circuited.
- Do not mix old and new batteries.
- Do not mix alkaline, standard (carbon-zinc) or rechargeable (nickel-cadmium) batteries.
- Prevent the book and unit from getting wet and avoid exposure to excessively hot or cold temperatures.
- Remove batteries when not in use or discharged.